Migratory birds in Europe

THEIR ROUTES, DESTINATIONS, AND BEHAVIOUR

HENK VAN DEN BRINK

 REBO PRODUCTIONS

© 1996 Zuid Boekprodukties, Lisse
© 1997 Published by Rebo Productions Ltd
Cover design: Ton Wienbelt, The Netherlands
Illustrations: Rik Slinger
Picture editing: TextCase, The Netherlands
Translation: Mary Boorman for First Edition Translations Ltd,
Great Britain
Typesetting: Hof&Land Typografie, The Netherlands

ISBN 1 901094 52 9

Contents

Foreword

There are people who almost daily each autumn, year after year, will get up very early in the morning, put on their warmest clothes, and in the early dawn go to a particular spot and sit there, with a thermos of coffee within reach. They will scan the sky and make a note of all the migrating birds which pass overhead. For a long time I belonged to that special company. Nowadays I prefer my sleep.

But I do treasure memories of the mornings when all the effort was richly rewarded – mornings when your eyes just could not take in the endless stream of finches, larks, thrushes, and geese which were passing overhead. Migratory birds do arouse interest and amazement, although you do not need to go quite so far as I used to. The interest leads to questions. Where do these birds come from? Where are they going to? What routes do they follow? How long does it take them? How do they find their way?

All these questions will be considered in this book although it is not intended to be an exhaustive study, and there is only a bird's eye view of each topic. It is intended for people who are curious about bird migration. The very keen bird-watcher will find in it a handy summary of all the information already acquired – and more.

The book will stimulate interest in migratory birds. That is the reason for the inclusion of a great many photographs. In many of them the birds have been caught on camera just as they are, so that you can almost feel the atmosphere. A word of thanks to the photographers is appropriate here, especially to Hans Hut who has taken care of the majority of the photographs. His shots reveal his great respect for birds. Perhaps this book can pass on something of that respect, in the hope that migratory birds will go on flying for us to enjoy.

Henk van den Brink

Introduction

This book is about migratory birds. These are birds that each year leave their breeding grounds and fly to their wintering grounds, and then return in the spring.

Young hobby. Hobbies eat many insects as well as small birds. They overwinter in southern Africa.

From the beginning of time migratory birds have fulfilled a symbolic role. All over mainland Europe there are celebrations when the storks return to their nesting sites. Swallows are the harbingers of spring.

In classical times the journeys of the cranes attracted attention. In the *Iliad*, the famous epic of the Trojan War, Homer compares the movements of the armies on the field of battle to the migration of the cranes in Asia Minor. For another Greek writer, Hesiod, the migration of the cranes symbolizes the changing seasons.

While the migration of the cranes is an amazing sight in itself, the movement of storks and swallows, and of many other birds, is less striking. One day in autumn they are gone, and one day in spring they are back with us again.

Although their coming and going has always attracted people's attention, for a very long time it was not known what actually happened to the birds while they were absent, and there were many strange explanations given.

It was thought that swallows spent the winter asleep in the mud at the bottom of ponds. Storks, too, were thought to hibernate. Then there were those birds that were believed to change into another species, like the cuckoo that became a sparrow hawk.

Some of these myths were very persistent. Even the famous Swedish biologist Linnaeus, as late as the eighteenth century, clung stubbornly to the story of the swallow in the mud.

Storks, bringers of new life. Sadly this sight is becoming more and more uncommon over large parts of Europe.

Yellow-browed warbler with ring. This little songbird breeds in the Siberian taiga and overwinters in southern Asia. Every autumn a number of yellow-browed warblers land in western Europe. Thanks to the ringing scheme more is known about their migration routes.

Serious study of bird migration dates from the last two centuries, and most of it is really very recent. In the past a person with field glasses was the exception but today in Western Europe there are hordes of bird watchers out and about. Elsewhere too bird watching is seen as much more usual. Knowledge about birds has increased enormously because the bird watchers record their observations systematically. The most important step forward in the study of bird migration was, however, the discovery of the technique of ringing birds.

Around 1900, the Danish schoolmaster Mortensen hit on the idea of catching birds and fitting them with a small aluminium ring round one leg, each ring having a numerical code and an address. Every ringed bird that is recovered – whether shot, caught, or killed accidentally – provides information about its journey.

Nowadays large birds such as geese and swans are fitted with coloured rings so that the living birds can be recognized in the field. Of course only a small percentage of the ringed birds are reported, but nevertheless in all kinds of places an enormous number of birds have been recorded in this way. Through the use of this technique we now have a broad picture of the wintering grounds of most of the birds which breed in Europe.

Following page: greylag geese in the Lauwersmeer.

The swallow with its cheerful twitter returns in the spring from Africa to liven up the countryside during the summer months.

7

The little gull breeds inland near fresh water and overwinters on the coast. The most important breeding grounds are the Baltic countries and Russia. In the winter little gulls spread out along the whole of the European coasts.

Previous page: waders.

Nowadays everyone knows that storks and swallows spend the winter in Africa. Through research very much more than that is known, for example that there are species that migrate even further, but also species that do not fly very far. The stopping places and the migration routes of many – but not all – species are known and the fact that there are birds which return year after year to exactly the same place to breed or to overwinter.

Information on the time of leaving, duration of the journey, and the altitude and speed of their flight is also available for many birds – radar observations have been invaluable here.

But, although the published work on research into bird migration would fill a large library, there is still a great deal that is not yet known.

Each answer throws up more questions. How do birds manage to find their particular place sometimes over distances of thousands of kilometres? Evidently birds have a good sense of direction, but where is it located? Is it inherited or acquired? How are birds able to find the ideal altitude? There are many unknown factors particularly as far as direction-finding is concerned.

There is so much still to be found out that even migration itself remains something of a mystery. Each new discovery simply makes bird migration even more fascinating.

A Bewick's swan being ringed.

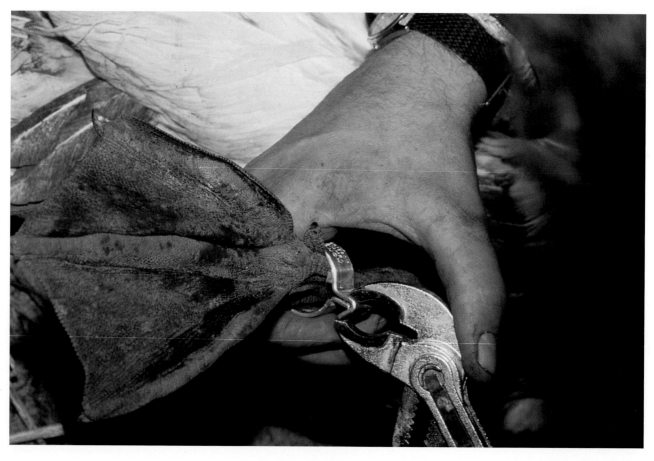

The migration of the cranes

The migration of the cranes is something that impresses everyone, because it reveals the immensity of the phenomenon of bird migration in all its immensity. The birds are impressive enough in themselves, with their huge, broad wings, with a span of more than two metres (six feet), their stately flight, their long legs, and their outstretched necks. They fly in lovely formations – in long lines and V formations. At the same time their call – a loud trumpet call – can be heard far in the distance.

For many people this call has an almost magical sound. Year in and year out, for centuries, the cranes have been following the same fixed routes from their breeding grounds in the marshes of Scandinavia and Russia to the south and back. Each year they gather at predetermined places at about the same time in spring and autumn. The Scandinavian cranes, for example, collect in their tens of thousands on the German island of Rügen in the Baltic, providing a spectacle that annually attracts bird-watchers from far and near.

The starling roosts

There are also directional and group movements which have nothing to do with migration. An example of this is the flight of the starlings to their roosts. Outside the breeding season the birds spend the night in communal sleeping roosts. Each evening as dusk approaches starlings from a wide area fly in together in groups to their roost, where the total numbers may be counted in tens of thousands.

The powerful flight of the cranes. Cranes breed in inaccessible marshes in northeastern Europe. They gather in large groups ready to migrate. They overwinter mainly in Spain and Turkey.

13

They use particular sites, often year after year. Some well-known roosts are in the middle of large towns, where the huge, noisy flocks of birds are quite spectacular but can on occasion be a nuisance.

Not only starlings use communal roosts – many members of the crow family, gulls, wading birds, swallows, and wagtails do so also.

The moult migration of the shelduck

Another mass movement is connected with the moult, as the regular renewal of birds' plumage is called. Ducks renew all their feathers at one time, which prevents them flying and makes them particularly vulnerable.

There are species that spend these dangerous periods together at fixed, safe sites. The flight to these places is known as moult migration.

The shelduck is a good example of a bird that migrates to moult. In July, as the moulting season approaches, all the shelduck from near and far migrate to the German Bight in the German part of the Wadden Sea, where they moult on the sand flats of the Knechtsand. In August there can be as many as 100,000 shelduck from the whole of western Europe.

Some come from as far afield as England, Ireland, and northern France. Shelduck also congregate in Bridgwater Bay in Somerset, for the moult.

Shelduck live on the coast. In the summer the adult shelduck migrate from their breeding grounds to the German Bight – an area between the mouths of the Rivers Weser and Elbe – to moult there.

Starlings flying to the roost.

The monarch is a
migratory butterfly
from America that can
cover thousands of
kilometres. From time
to time one lands in
Europe, usually as a
stowaway on a ship,
but sometimes
perhaps under its own
steam. This specimen
was photographed on
Madeira.

**Migration of
butterflies, fishes,
and reindeer**

Regular migration over long distances is not confined to birds. Many other members of the animal kingdom do so, for example some butterflies, fishes, and mammals. Although butterflies seem to flap about rather clumsily compared with birds, there are species that migrate. The best-known example of this is the monarch butterfly in North America which migrates over a distance of about 5,000km (3,000 miles) from Canada to Mexico. A European example is the red admiral, which reaches north Africa from Scandinavia. Locusts are another famous example of winged insects that migrate.

Migration is a widespread phenomenon among fish and other aquatic creatures. You have only to think of the salmon which leaves the sea and swims upstream in the rivers to spawn far inland. Eels make the journey in reverse – from the rivers to the ocean.

But there are animals too, that walk over huge distances, such as the reindeer in Lapland and Siberia, which every year journey hundreds of kilometres between their summer and winter grounds.

Male tufted ducks.

*Following page:
cranes on Rügen.
Families remain
together in the group.
In the middle of the
group a parent bird
watches his young
landing.*

15

Why do birds migrate?

This chapter includes a discussion as to why some birds remain in the same place the whole year round, while others travel each year great distances in summer or winter to breed or overwinter.

In an English garden there are the same blackbirds in winter as in the summer. In a Dutch garden, however, the winter blackbird is probably different from the summer one. It is highly likely that the winter blackbird is a visitor from Scandinavia or eastern Europe.

Some birds are only here during the summer. The swallows, the stork, and the cuckoo were mentioned in the previous chapter, but various song birds such as the reed warbler depart after the summer. Other birds only spend the winter here, such as geese, various species of duck, and the redwing.

These are all migratory birds. You see some birds here the whole year round, such as the house sparrow, the blackbird, the robin, and the chaffinch. At first sight you would say that they are sedentary birds, or species that do not migrate but that is, however, not the case.

Although you think that the robin and the blackbird in your garden is the same one all the year round, in reality they are different groups. There is a continual displacement taking place in which starlings, blackbirds, and robins from western Europe migrate to England, France, and Spain and are replaced by members of the same species from regions further north and east.

Even house sparrows appear to migrate. In fact there seem to be very few truly sedentary birds, a few examples of which are the magpie, the grey partridge, and the goshawk.

Reasons for remaining

The question "why do birds migrate?" could really be turned round to read "why do some birds not migrate?"

Apparently migration is a successful strategy. It is true that migrating

Male house sparrow. From time to time birds, mainly young ones, are seen on migration.

Page 18: black-necked grebe.

Page 19: many spotted redshanks migrate in a broad front from the tundras directly to their African winter quarters. Thousands of them, however, follow the route along the coast of western Europe.

Moorhen. After a severe winter the numbers have been decimated The population has often recovered within a couple of years.

birds run a great many risks – they begin an uncertain journey which could be disastrous for them – but the risks run by sedentary birds in northern regions are at least as great.

Many birds succumb when their food becomes unobtainable because of snow and ice. After a severe winter the numbers of moorhens and kingfishers are only a fraction of what they were the previous year. The damage can be repaired within a couple of years by the birds laying many eggs and rearing many young successfully.

Thus birds, as it were, weigh the costs of staying and the costs of leaving against each other.

The determining factor is food – there must be enough food available and the birds must be able to reach it without having to pay too high a price in energy. For most insect eaters, such as swallows, food is not available in the breeding grounds in winter. They must therefore migrate southwards.

Under normal circumstances it pays sedentary birds to remain in the breeding area, because they can still find enough food. It is not for nothing that the omnivores that profit from human scraps, such as the carrion crow and the magpie, remain here in winter.

The goshawk, too, can remain in its breeding area during the winter. It is a bird of prey that eats mainly other birds and there are still plenty of those about in the winter. With snow and ice there will be less prey but against that they will be easier to catch.

Swallows are only seen here in the summer. They build their nests of mud and straw, often in large colonies, on ledges in buildings or on rock ledges. They spend the winter in Africa.

If you want to have robins breeding in your garden feeding them in winter will not always help, because the winter ones may be different from the summer ones.

The goshawk does have to adapt considerably since it has to move its hunting ground from the woodland, where it is active in the summer, to the larger territory of open fields. From the foregoing it will be apparent that in the winter many of the so-called sedentary birds are less tied to a place than in the breeding season, and that in spite of that description they can in fact lead a wandering existence.

For some species, such as the white wagtail and the grey heron, the risks of staying and leaving are about evenly balanced. With those species you will also see that part of the population moves away, while another part stays.

Reasons for migrating

It will be clear that the further north birds breed the more likely it is that the balance will be in favour of migrating, and the further south they breed, the more likely it is that they will decide to remain where they are. Thus buzzards are sedentary birds in central Europe, and migratory in Scandinavia. In winter the Scandinavian buzzards go in search of members of the family in central Europe. Blackbirds, robins, and chaffinches that breed in Great Britain remain there in the winter and then have the company of members of the species from Scandinavia and mainland Europe.

A buzzard in a characteristic pose. In northern Europe the buzzard is a migratory bird, but in the south it is sedentary.

Breeding ground as starting point

The question as to why birds migrate looks a simple one to answer but appearances are deceptive.

It actually depends on how you approach the question. Probably because people associate birds' nests with the house, a fixed place to which they return after a journey, they tend to chose the viewpoint of the breeding bird and take the breeding ground as a starting point. But this is not a valid comparison at all. The only function of nests is as a place to rear young.

The whole breeding season, from building the nest until the young leave it, only takes up a few months at the most. That is also the reason why "our" breeding birds, the summer visitors, are only here for a short time. The rest of the year is taken up by migration and overwintering.

Frozen tufts of reeds, frozen berries; there is nothing left here for the birds.

Winter quarters as starting point

A spoonbill colony on Texel. The birds choose their nesting sites in a marsh on the edge of the water to make it as difficult as possible for predators.

Given that migration and overwintering take up the greater part of the year it is really more logical to consider it from the angle of the bird in its winter quarters. The question then is why birds migrate to other regions to breed.

The answer is suddenly not so very obvious. Why should storks and swallows, that have evidently had sufficient food throughout the winter in Africa, set off on an uncertain journey to the north where they have to wait to find out if there will be enough food? Why do Brent geese from the Dutch Wadden Sea, where they have eaten their fill, migrate to the Siberian tundra, which in all probability will still be covered by snow and ice?

The fox poses one of the threats to eggs and young birds.

The answer is – because of their young. In their winter quarters there is too much competition from native breeding birds, often sedentary birds, which already occupy the most favourable territories. The winter visitors end up in the less rich places and are often driven to lead a wandering existence, something that they cannot afford to do in the breeding season.

In the breeding season it is not enough for there to be sufficient food for the parent birds, there must also be enough for the young. It must be good-quality food, so that they can thrive, and it must be available in large quantities in the few weeks that the young are growing.

Furthermore, it must be concentrated in a small area so that the parents do not have to spend time making long flights in search of food. The wintering grounds cannot fulfil these conditions.

It is not, however, merely a question of food, there are other requirements that must be satisfied. For example, there must be a suitable place available for a nest. This must be protected from enemies as far as possible.

In the Wadden area nests and young of Brent geese, knot, and grey plover would have very little chance against predators such as gulls and crows. On the tundra these enemies are not absent altogether, but in the wide spaces of the tundra their density is much less. Partly because of their perfect camouflage the birds run less risk. Then the tundra, with its short but very productive growing season satisfies the

Fulmars spend the whole year at sea, only coming ashore to breed. They nest on cliffs, often on small islands, which are inaccessible for predators.

other main condition – at the right time there is an abundance of food. You have only to think of the billions of midges that can make life a misery.

Inborn internal annual rhythm

The question of why birds migrate can be approached from yet another direction – not from the advantage for the species but from the angle of the individual bird. How does a bird know when it its time to migrate?

It is easy to answer this in the case of species that only leave when there is a reason, for example when rivers freeze over, when the ground is frozen or snow-covered, so that food is unobtainable.

But species that travel great distances between breeding grounds and winter quarters leave the breeding grounds very much earlier. They do it before the very first signs of winter. Some migrate in the middle of summer, when there is still plenty of food, because the birds will then have enough time and they will have sufficient food on the journey.

Experiments which were done with birds in cages have shown that birds have an inborn annual rhythm. This physiologically determined rhythm governs the timing of all kinds of processes in the life of the bird, including migration. Under the influence of this rhythm around a certain date a bird spontaneously begins to exhibit the urge to migrate – the caged birds become restless. This rhythm is probably driven by day length.

Following page: flight of wild duck.

Pages 30-31: geese in a real Dutch winter scene.

Oystercatchers spend the winter in huge numbers in the Wadden area. They only migrate in severe frosts.

In August or the beginning of September the yellow wagtail migrates southward once again.

27

Destinations

Some migratory birds travel huge distances annually between their breeding grounds and winter quarters, while others remain where they are or at the most move a short distance when the frost comes. Many European breeding birds overwinter in Africa, but there are also a number that do not leave Europe.

Long-distance migrants

As far as distance is concerned, the arctic tern beats all the records. Arctic terns breed in the northern polar regions, including the most northerly piece of land on earth – the north point of Greenland. During the long arctic winter they are living under the midnight sun in the south polar regions, on the edge of the extensive antarctic pack ice. No other bird species experiences so much daylight.

The return journey over the Atlantic Ocean is certainly 30,000km (19,000 miles). There are probably arctic terns that fly the equivalent of a journey round the earth. If a tern lives for 25 years – and that does happen – it can have flown a million kilometres (625,000 miles) in its lifetime!

The arctic tern is the world record-holder for long-distance flights. But there are other species that achieve almost as much, such as the shearwater, distant relative of the albatross, which wander across the entire Atlantic Ocean, or the ruff, which migrates from eastern Siberia to central Africa.

And even small song birds, such as the northern wheatear from Alaska, fly across Asia to southern Africa. Many European song birds also cover unbelievable distances in order to overwinter in southern Africa. Compared with this the effort made by the impressive cranes described in the introduction is very modest.

With their journey from Scandinavia to southwestern Spain they are only average.

The arctic tern flies very gracefully.

Above left: an arctic tern on the nest in a typical breeding habitat.

Opposite page: the record journey of the arctic tern – from pole to pole.

***Short and
middle-distance
migrants***

*Male shoveler.
Males and females
winter separately:
the males winter
nearer to the
breeding grounds.*

By no means all migratory birds make impressive journeys. Some chaffinches and starlings only make a modest trip of a few hundred kilometres, for example from the Netherlands or north Germany to France. And then there are bad-weather migrants that only move a short distance when the frost takes hold, such as some skylarks, meadow pipits, oystercatchers, and curlews that migrate less than 100km (60 miles).

With many species that migrate over short or medium distances the differences in winter quarters and length of journey are related to age and sex. Males migrate less far than females and adult birds less far than young ones.

That sometimes leads to distinct zones – a zone with almost all males and a zone with almost all young birds. This variation in migration behaviour can be clearly seen among, for example, blackbirds, chaffinches, and shoveler. The males return first to the breeding grounds, where they can meanwhile stake out their territory in anticipation of the females' return.

Older males return before young males so that they can find the best sites. Perhaps the older birds are more resistant to the winter weather and are therefore in a better position to withstand bad weather in the breeding season. In any case the result is that older birds have on balance more chance of breeding success.

Below left: the northern wheatear, which only measures 15cm (6in) from beak to tail, covers impressive distances of up to 11,000km (7,000 miles).

Below right: ruff in full plumage. Ruffs migrate from eastern Siberia to Kenya.

Winter destinations of European breeding birds

The majority of migratory birds that breed in Europe have Africa as their winter destination. The Mediterranean region is in second place. Many birds from Scandinavia and Siberia overwinter in western Europe.

It is far from always the case that the winter quarters are south of the breeding grounds. Geese, swans, and waders from Siberia overwinter in western Europe.

Of the starlings, thrushes, and chaffinches from the northwest of the European continent, a proportion crosses the North Sea to spend the winter in England or Ireland.

Africa: insect eaters

Where birds spend the winter depends mainly on what they eat. The contingent that heads for Africa consists largely of bird species that live on insects and small creatures.

When you look more closely, it appears that the group consists of birds that catch insects on the wing or on the surface of leaves, stems, and such like, including swallows, whitethroats, garden warblers, and flycatchers.

Birds that take small prey from the trunks and branches of trees, such as woodpeckers, tits, and treecreepers, can still survive in the north. They do not migrate very far, if at all. The same applies to species that seek their food on or in the soil, like blackbirds and robins.

Following page: an arctic tern.

Apart from insect-eaters, members of the African contingent include

Bewick's swans breed on Novaya Zemlya and the Taymyr peninsula in Siberia.

Water pipits from the Alps sometimes winter in the Netherlands and north Germany, thus north of their breeding grounds.

35

species that take fish and other animal food from the surface of the water. Terns such as the common tern, sandwich tern, and black tern are good examples.

The sedge warbler also suffered during the great drought in the Sahara in the early seventies.

Life in Africa in the winter

The migratory birds from Europe that spend the winter months in Africa do not head for the luxuriant tropical rain forest as you might expect. By far the majority of the birds can be found in less fertile, dry regions – the savanna and even the grasslands. Here conditions are very changeable, but the birds are attuned to this. The migrating birds arrive during the rainy season and they go in search of places where rain falls from time to time. In these places it is a case of a short-term rich vegetation, which means there is also an abundance of insects. Bee-eaters, shrikes, flycatchers, and other species plunder such places.

The frequent fires also often provide a useful source of food. Large numbers of migrant birds congregate round the scenes of fires to take advantage of the swarms of fleeing insects. Places where a fire has burnt out also provide a lot of food.

In addition, the species has undergone a structural decline in numbers. There are therefore other factors involved, of which the most important is the drying out and pollution of the marshes in Europe which provide its breeding habitat.

Bee-eaters breed in the Mediterranean region and in the Balkans. They winter in southern Africa.

Migrants will sometimes travel hundreds of kilometres in search of good feeding grounds. This is not an easy existence. The Sahel region south of the Sahara is an important wintering ground for many migrants. This seemed to be a risky strategy around 1970, when the rains failed year after year. It was a disaster not only in human terms but also for the migrant birds. Species that winter there, such as whitethroats and sedge warblers, were dealt a heavy blow. There was a drastic reduction in their numbers.

Europe: divers and omnivores

Some insect eaters go over to a vegetarian diet in winter. They do migrate, but only over short distances. Fieldfares and redwings, for example, live mainly on berries. They do not need to leave Europe in order to find berries. Great tits and blue tits often include beechnuts in their winter menu, or peanuts from the bird-table. A good example of a bird that changes its diet radically in the winter is the bearded tit. The bearded tit is a bird that lives in reed beds and eats insects in the summer and reed seeds in the winter. Its digestive system and gut even adapt to this change in diet.

Water birds, too, that catch fish and other food by diving, do not usually move so far away either. There are enough areas in Europe where the water does not freeze over. Along the North Sea coast and round the Mediterranean there are important wintering grounds for divers, great crested grebes, cormorants, and diving ducks such as the tufted duck.

The true omnivores, such as gulls and crows, seed eaters such as finches and buntings, and grazing birds, such as geese and wigeon, also remain in Europe.

There are three distinct populations of Brent geese. The breeding birds form Novaya Zemlya winter in the Netherlands, those from Spitsbergen in Scotland (Solway Firth), and the breeding birds from Greenland in Scotland and Ireland.

The black-headed gull is a true omnivore. It is very flexible in its migration behaviour, with winter quarters that vary from southern Scandinavia to north Africa.

Following page: cormorants are good divers and eat fish.

Variations within the species

There can often be great variations in winter destination within the same species. In Chapter 2 it was mentioned that buzzards from northern Europe migrate southwards, while members of the species that breed further south remain in their breeding grounds during the winter. There are also species in which all birds migrate, but in which birds from the north migrate to more distant destinations than the ones from the south. So birds from northern breeding grounds pass their more southerly relations on the way to their winter quarters. A good example of a bird that migrates in this "leap-frog" pattern is the ringed plover.

Ringed plovers from Lapland and Siberia migrate to central and southern Africa, while other members of the species from southern Sweden migrate to north Africa, and others that breed in Denmark, northern Germany, and the Netherlands have southern France and Spain as their final destination. The ringed plovers that breed in the British Isles remain where they are.

Breeding ringed plover. It prefers to nest on a shingle beach or shell bank and makes no more than a slight hollow.

Bird invasions

Opposite page: The "leap-frog" migration of the ringed plover – the further north the birds breed the further south they migrate.

There is a very special category of migration known as invasion or eruption. Every few years the birds involved suddenly appear in places where they would scarcely, if ever, be seen. These invasions can be so spectacular that they even attract the attention of the least knowledgeable and get a mention in the press. The invasions of the waxwing and the nutcracker are famous examples.

Ringed plovers in the migration season.

Beechnuts, not abundant every year.

Events leading up to an invasion always follow the same pattern. If one year has an exceptionally good harvest of a species' favourite food – rowan berries in the case of the waxwing, pine seeds for the nut-cracker – the population will rise significantly. Consequently, the following year's harvest will not be sufficient to feed the increased bird population.

The combination of high numbers and shortage of food compels the birds to migrate from their normal areas. Eruptions therefore occur mainly with species that have a fluctuating source of food – some years there is a surplus and some years a shortage. That applies, for example, to tree seeds.

Trees and shrubs live a long time and do not need to put a lot of energy into seed production. Their tactics usually consist of producing a great deal of seed in a good year and very little in a poor year. Birds that feed exclusively on the seeds or fruit of trees are therefore often compelled to adopt a wandering lifestyle.

A good example of such a bird is the magpie, which outside the breeding season lives mainly on acorns.

Other invasion birds are the brambling which lives mainly on beechnuts, the siskin, which needs alder cones, and the redpoll, which eats mainly birch seeds. Eruptions of insect eaters, which switch to a diet of tree seeds in winter, can also occur, including great tits (beechnuts) and coal tits (fir seeds).

In autumn and winter the magpie lives mainly on acorns. Some years there are very many and other years they are scarce. In years with a poor harvest magpies seek refuge and large invasions occur.

Pages 46-47:
male bearded tit.

Pages 48-49: an arctic
tern feeding its young.

Pages 50-51:
cranes on an autumn
morning.

The short-eared owl
eats mainly voles.
It leads an irregular,
wandering existence,
because it is always
searching for places
with an abundance
of field voles.
Invasions of short-
eared owls coincide
with the cyclical
pattern of the field
vole population.

The true nomad among the birds is the crossbill which is specially adapted to eating the seeds of fir trees. It can extract the seeds from the cones with its beak. Fir cones are abundant one year and scarce the next. The birds lead a wandering existence searching for woods with a plentiful harvest.

Certain species of small mammal, particularly the field vole, form another variable food source. In some years there are invasions of birds of prey and owls which are dependent on such sources of food, including the rough-legged buzzard and the short-eared owl. The occurrence of voles often shows a more or less fixed pattern, with peaks every so many years. The eruptions of birds of prey follow this pattern.

A juvenile glaucus
gull can be distin-
guished from a
juvenile herring gull
by its light wing tips.
Glaucus gulls breed
in the inhospitable
world of rocks, snow,
and ice in the arctic
regions. In winter
they roam over the
most northerly coasts
of Europe.

Migration routes and stopping places

This chapter discusses the routes that the migratory birds take to their winter quarters, as well as how they cope with the obstacles they encounter on the way, and where they stop to refuel in order to be able to complete their journey.

Migration routes

Which routes do birds follow from their breeding grounds to their winter quarters and vice versa? You could say that if you can fly you will have little problem with obstacles and you merely take the shortest route from A to B. You stop off on the way at a suitable place to eat and rest when you are tired.

Many birds do indeed take the shortest route from A to B – at least for a part of the journey. They fly on a broad front, irrespective of the landscape that stretches out beneath them. But in some cases that landscape below does pose some problems and they have to deviate from the shortest route.

During their flight the birds can encounter high mountains, such as the Alps and the Pyrenees, and they have to cross wide stretches of water such as the North Sea and the Mediterranean in one hop. Some birds also have to fly over enormous areas of the Sahara desert. How they cope with these obstacles is discussed below.

Coping with obstacles

Some birds take no notice of the Alps and simply fly high across them.

These birds are physically equipped to fly at great altitudes. Other birds cross them through the passes, which leads to noticeable concentrations in narrow migration corridors. But there are birds – probably the majority – that when they leave choose a route that allows them to avoid the Alps altogether.

The migration of the knot (here in winter plumage) appeals to the imagination. Knots from Canada and Greenland migrate – non-stop or with a break in Iceland – to their winter quarters on the British coast and in the Wadden Sea. The knots that breed in Siberia migrate non-stop to the Wadden Sea, and from there, again without stopping, to Mauritania.

The strategy adopted to avoid the mountains varies from species to species and sometimes within a species.

There is no general rule, but it is clear that the weather plays an important role.

In good weather – dry, sunny, and a following wind – birds fly higher and they take less notice of the landscape below them.

Some birds, even small song birds, usually cross the Mediterranean Sea directly in one go.

Many birds migrate through Spain or Italy, in order to have a short sea crossing, and others, particularly from eastern Europe, fly via Greece, Turkey, and Israel avoiding the sea altogether. The weather probably influences whether they cross the sea directly or make a detour to avoid it.

Young kittiwake. Kittiwakes are elegant fliers, which spend much of the year roaming the Atlantic Ocean. They come ashore in summer to breed. Like most sea birds they breed along rocky coasts.

Preparations for the journey

Thanks to the fat reserves they have built up, migrating birds are equipped physically to cross an enormous distance at one time.

Before and during the journey the birds eat much more than normal. The extra food is stored in the body as fat which serves as fuel. At the start of the journey the birds are noticeably heavier than during the rest of the year.

In the spring garden warblers in central Africa that were about to begin the journey to the north were found to weigh about 30g (1oz). This is almost twice their normal weight of 17g (0.6oz). This increase

in weight is coupled with a strengthening of the muscles, since the extra weight has to be carried. In theory birds build up enough fat reserves to be able to cross the Sahara plus the Mediterranean Sea non-stop. Probably some do in fact do that, although this has not yet been proved.

Stork

Thermals   Birds that travel mainly by gliding, such as storks, buzzards, honey buzzards, eagles, and other birds of prey, have specific migration routes. They take advantage of the principle that warm air rises. The rising currents of warm air are known as thermals. In certain weather conditions these form thermal bubbles in which the birds can circle round and be carried to high altitudes, from which they can then glide in the direction of their migration. In this way they can travel tens of kilometres without once moving their wings.

Thermals only form over land, so that the birds which make use of them have to avoid the open sea. That means detours over land and great concentrations of birds at the shortest sea crossings. These places work like a funnel.

Opposite page: the migration routes of the stork. Because storks do not like to travel over the sea there are "funnels" at Gibraltar and in the Bosphorus.

One of these sites is Falsterno in southern Sweden, which is famous for the large groups of birds of prey – buzzards, honey buzzards – that pass through in the spring. Every year the sight of so many birds of prey attracts crowds of bird watchers who come in their hundreds to watch the migration. The concentrations of birds at Gibraltar and the

A cumulus cloud shows the presence of thermals. Cumulus clouds form in sunny but unstable conditions, with rising warm air. Thermals are ideal for birds that glide such as the buzzard and the stork.

55

Bosphorus near Istanbul are even more spectacular. The buzzards and honey buzzards are joined here by kites, eagles, and other birds of prey, not forgetting the storks.

On a good day there will be thousands of storks crossing by the Bosphorus – the air is thick with them. I cannot imagine anyone there not being impressed by the sight!

Filling stations on the eastern Atlantic coastal route

Apart from birds of prey there is yet another group of birds for which the shortest route is not appropriate. To be able to take the shortest route the birds must be able not only to avoid obstacles but also to be able to find suitable stopping places with sufficient food during the journey.

Some birds are restricted to certain stopping places either because of the type of food they eat or their specific way of feeding. Their route must therefore take them from one stopping place to the next. It would be nice if these happened to lie in a straight line between the summer and winter quarters.

A pattern of migration like that occurs particularly with wading birds that feed in inter-tidal areas and in river estuaries. They breed on the tundra in Greenland, Lapland, and Siberia.

Their most important stopping places are situated along the coasts of the North Sea and the Atlantic Ocean – the Wadden Sea, British coastal areas, and a couple of river deltas on the French and Spanish

Opposite page: the East Atlantic Flyway – migration route for millions of waders and geese.

The greenshank is a small wader that is not dependent on particular areas for its food. You can come across it near the smallest pools and ditches. It migrates on a broad front across the European mainland.

Wadden area, stopping place for millions of migrating birds.

The dunlin is the commonest wader on the East Atlantic Flyway.

coasts. They winter along the coasts of Morocco and Mauritania. Every year millions of birds follow this route which is known as the "East Atlantic Flyway."

The bar-tailed godwit and the knot are famous for the great distances they can travel non-stop. In the spring they often fly in one hop from Mauritania to the Wadden Sea.

There they replenish their fat reserves, in order to fly again non-stop to their breeding grounds. Both legs are 4,000 to 5,000km (2,500 to 3,000 miles) long. The birds have to fly non-stop because there are no other suitable resting places on the way. This emphasizes how much the continued existence of these species depends on these areas still being available.

The narrow margins of the bar-tailed godwit

Birds which breed on the Siberian tundra have very little time to raise their young. They have to do it in the two summer months. Before the abundant but very short-lived food sources fail the birds must have left.

But areas where they can spend the rest of the year are in short supply. Many species head for the Wadden Sea. For some of them this is their final destination, but for the majority it is "only" a halt on the way to Africa.

These birds have a hurried existence and life is a constant struggle to survive. This is true for the bar-tailed godwit. For years the Dutch

Opposite page: twites can be seen in winter especially on the coast. They often scratch about for seeds in large groups on salt marshes among the glasswort and sea-aster. They are restless birds that are always moving about. In central Europe they occur far inland during the winter, in the east of Germany, Poland, and the Czech Republic.

Bar-tailed godwits.

Brent geese grazing. The young lack the white collar of the older birds. Sometimes the geese arrive without young. The whole breeding season has been a failure. This is thought to be indirectly connected to the lemming cycle: if there are few lemmings the arctic fox has to make do with the young of the Brent geese. Weather also plays a role: if spring arrives too late on the tundra there is insufficient time to bring up the young.

biologist Theunis Piersma has followed the life of this bird step by step. The following story is largely taken from his research.

It begins in the winter on the Banc d'Arguin, an area of mud flats by the coast of Mauritania in west Africa, the most important wintering ground for the bar-tailed godwit.

The winter is relatively the most restful period in the birds' life. At this time they need only eat sufficient to live. The resting season is over at the beginning of March. The moult begins and the males exchange their pale grey-brown winter plumage for a handsome deep brownish-red plumage while the females become light reddish. At the same time the birds have to lay down fat reserves in order to have enough fuel for the coming journey.

The bar-tailed godwits now spend every available moment feeding, both day and night. Their diet consists mainly of shellfish and other bottom-living sea creatures.

If they get behind in their schedule they omit part of the moult. The birds that do not moult fully remain rather pale. At the end of April they leave for the Wadden Sea, a journey of 4,500km (2,800 miles) which takes three days non-stop.

They have enough fat reserves to make the journey in one hop, provided the circumstances are favourable. They must have a following wind to be able to fly fast enough. They therefore search for the layer of air in which the wind is favourable.

The curlew sandpiper keeps the grey plover company in the far north of Siberia. It has two or two and a half months at the most to breed and bring up the young. After that it flies at top speed to the wintering grounds which extend from South Africa to New Zealand.

Brent geese that breed in Taymir (Siberia) winter on the North Sea coasts of England and France. In the spring they spend time in the Wadden Sea area before they return to their breeding grounds with a stop over by the White Sea.

The wind direction at high altitudes is often different from that lower down. It seems that bar-tailed godwits are able to find the correct altitude, not only at the start but also throughout the whole journey. If a favourable wind cannot be found anywhere they have problems. They take too long over the journey, their fat reserves are used up, and they have to make an intermediate stop to refuel in areas that are not suitable for it.

If all goes well and the birds do reach the Wadden Sea in one hop, then they are completely exhausted. Their fuel reserves have been used up and their stomachs are shrunken. When they have regained their strength they will start eating again.

The males that are already reddish become even redder, while the pale birds are further behind, since they have already had difficulty replenishing their fat reserves. If they do manage to, there is still a good chance that they will not find a partner in the breeding grounds. Among the bar-tailed godwits the rule is the redder the better when it comes to finding a mate. The pale birds are failures that you do not fancy starting a family with.

From the Wadden Sea they again fly non-stop about 5,000km (3,000 miles) to the breeding grounds. That means that they have to fly at intervals of a few days behind each other. They reach the breeding grounds at the beginning of June.

If everything has gone well, they still have a little in reserve to be able

Grey plover in winter plumage. Grey plovers breed exclusively in the far northern tundra, on the coast of the Arctic Ocean. After the breeding season they hurry to the Wadden Sea. When they have regained their strength most of them migrate further along the Atlantic coast. Many grey plovers also winter on the British coast.

to start breeding, and with luck the snow is beginning to melt. If that is not the case the birds have to wait or even retrace their journey a little way.

That must not take up too much time or they will have to forget about breeding for that season. In good weather the eggs are laid within a week. If the nesting site has been well chosen and the clutch is not eaten by an arctic fox or a stoat the young birds will hatch in three weeks.

When the young have hatched the female bird leaves the breeding ground immediately and flies straight back to the Wadden Sea, leaving the care of the young entirely to the male. That is a full-time job even though the young birds look for food for themselves – mainly insects – almost straight away. The male must warm the chicks regularly and protect them from predators, such as gulls, that are on the prowl.

If the young are reared successfully, after three weeks the male himself returns to the Wadden Sea, leaving the young to fend for themselves. A couple of weeks later they too will go by themselves to the Wadden Sea. This journey, too, takes a couple of days.

In the Wadden Sea the bar-tailed godwits again eat their fill, while the older birds moult once again, this time from summer to winter plumage. Then the bar-tailed godwits migrate once again non-stop to the west coast of Africa and the whole cycle begins again. The above

The marsh sandpiper is a rare sight. It breeds deep in the Russian interior and winters in Africa and Asia. From time to time a few penetrate to the west.

Turnstones winter on rocky coasts and some migrate thousands of kilometres over open sea.

description also applies to the knot, and in broad outline to the dunlin, grey plover, and Brent goose. It illustrates the narrow margins of a migratory bird's existence, in which everything has to fit and nothing must go wrong, and every mistake and set-back is fatal. When you realize that, you are amazed that so many birds reach their destination every year.

A bird's-eye view of the coast as the bird approaches land. This is a glimpse that creates so much anxiety for birds that they adjust their course and fly parallel to the coast. Birds that cross at high altitudes in general take no notice of the coastline.

Common scoter breed in Scandinavia and Siberia. They moult in late summer in great hordes on the North Sea, kilometres from land. Sometimes they winter there and sometimes they fly further along the Atlantic coast.

Pages 64-65: bar-tailed godwits.

Pages 66-67: dunlin and grey plovers on the mud flats.

The journey

How fast do birds fly and at what altitude? Do they prefer to fly during the day or at night? Do they migrate alone or in groups? You will find the answers to all these questions in this chapter.

How fast do migrating birds fly?

During migration most birds fly on average rather faster than usual. Chaffinches reach 40km (25 miles) an hour, about the same as the swift, which can reach higher maximum speeds. An average of 60km (40 miles) per hour has been recorded for the wood pigeon. Ducks and geese fly at 70-90km (45-60 miles) an hour. At those speeds birds would be able to cross Europe in a couple of days if they flew steadily, and be deep in the African interior within a couple of weeks. But it rarely happens like that. Migratory birds are certainly not champions involved in a race against the clock.

They take it calmly especially in the autumn. Most birds take months to reach their winter quarters. They usually fly for only a few hours a day, in which they will cover roughly 150km (100 miles).

The remainder of the time they spend eating and resting. That is very necessary, because migrating uses up energy, and they must replace that by eating well.

Then there are days when they will not fly at all, so that over all they will average 50-75km (30-45 miles) a day.

That seems to contradict what was said in the previous chapter about birds crossing the Mediterranean Sea and the Sahara in one go, and some birds flying thousands of kilometres at a time, from one stopping place to another.

But birds will only do that if there is really no alternative. They can do it if they have to, but if not they will avoid it.

Opposite page: black-winged stilts are mainly found in southern Europe but they occasionally breed in northern Europe. They over-winter in Africa.

Wood pigeon.

Above left: the dunnock is a rather insignificant little bird. Breeding birds from the north and east of Europe are migratory. Dunnocks avoid each other's company both during migration and in the winter.

Following page: most night fliers leave in the dusk, probably because the position of the setting sun helps them to fix their course.

At what time of the day do migrating birds fly?

The greater part of migration takes place without us noticing because most birds migrate at night. Anyone who is listening can from time to time hear the thin call of the redwing, the short chucking sound of the song thrush, or the gabble of a flock of geese. On cloudy evenings, when the lights from built-up areas are reflected by the clouds, you can sometimes see the geese flying past.

Almost all the long-distance migrants (especially insect eaters) travel at night, like most ducks, geese, and waders. During the day there is more time to look for food, and furthermore, flying in the cooler, more rarefied air uses less energy. Perhaps the fact that at night there is usually less wind is also a factor.

Many short-distance migrants, principally seed eaters, and of course birds that glide and therefore need the thermal currents, travel during the day. The only long-distance migrants that fly during the day are the swallows. They catch insects on the wing, so that they can eat and travel at the same time.

The night journey begins at dusk, about half an hour after sunset. All the nocturnal migrants leave about the same time, as if on command. The explanation may be that this is a favourable time to plot a course – the place where the sun went down is still visible, while the stars are beginning to appear in the sky.

Like most waders the common sandpiper travels at night. In May and August its call can be heard from time to time in the dark – a sharp, piping note.

The grasshopper warbler is one of the many song birds that migrates at night.

After several hours the journey slackens off, because most birds then pack up again.

Most diurnal migrants leave in the half hour before sunrise. The most intensive movement is during the morning. Only the thermal migrants travel during the middle of the day, when the earth has warmed up sufficiently for the thermal currents to develop.

Swallows congregating before departure.

Migration in groups

Outside the breeding season most birds live in groups. Many birds also migrate in groups, especially species that travel during the day. These can vary in size from small groups of a few birds to flocks of ten thousand or more. The groups take on a variety of forms. The most impressive are the V-shaped formations of waders, cranes, ducks, and geese. For many people the V-shaped formation is the symbol of bird migration.

In such a V-shaped formation the leading position is taken in turn by a different bird, as it is in a cycling team.

Migrating in a group can have several advantages, among them better protection from predators. The birds can also pass on information to each other, for example about good feeding sites. On the principle that "two heads are better than one" groups can probably navigate better.

Living in groups means quite a significant change compared with the

A V-formation of white-fronted geese.

life of the birds during the breeding season, when they live in pairs and family units. Sometimes you see that the social pressure, the tendency to seek out members of the same species, really has to be built up.

A family of whooper swans. The young remain in the middle.

At the moment of writing – at the end of August – I can see this development taking place among the swallows round my house. A few weeks ago the birds were still divided into separate families, but gradually swallows in the area began to congregate, especially in the evenings.

That happens more and more often and with bigger numbers. They often sit on the roof and on the aerials, but from time to time they will all fly round making their twittering noises – as if they are practising for the real work to come.

Flocks of migrating birds do not always consist of one species. Particular combinations of species often occur, such as groups of chaffinches and bramblings, redwings and fieldfares, or white-fronted and Brent geese. In these cases it is a matter of closely related species, but that does not always have to be the case. Chaffinches can migrate together with larks, and starlings can travel with fieldfares and so on.

The red-crested pochard breeds in the reed beds of lakes and deltas in eastern and southern Europe. It migrates over short distances.

At what altitude do birds fly?

You can literally climb the highest mountain in the world with great pain and effort and danger to yourself, only to see a flock of geese flying overhead as if it is nothing at all. That did happen to a group of

climbers on Mount Everest, at about 8,800m (29,000ft). The geese in question were bar-headed geese. Other tough specimens are known from Europe. Over the Hebrides a plane encountered a flock of swans at an altitude of 8,300m (26,500ft), where the temperature was down to -40°C (-40°F)!

Birds can therefore fly at tremendous altitudes, but in general migration takes place at much lower levels. Most birds do not fly higher than 1km (3,200ft), while the majority of them even remain below 500m (1,500ft).

During the night they fly at a higher altitude than during the day, and higher over the sea than over land.

Birds adapt their altitude to the weather – mainly to the wind. They fly at very low levels in strong winds, sometimes just above the ground because the wind close to the ground is always less strong than higher up.

Birds fly higher with a following wind. Birds are even able to find higher layers in the air in which they have a favourable wind. This tactic is applied particularly by birds that travel long distances without stopping such as the bar-tailed godwit, which flies non-stop from Africa to the Wadden Sea. Finding a favourable wind in a higher layer can be literally a matter of life and death for these birds, because if they are unsuccessful they run the risk of not reaching their destina-

The Montagu's harrier is a true summer visitor that in August is already leaving its breeding ground en route for tropical Africa. The migration occurs on a broad front, which means the Mediterranean Sea forms no barrier.

Wigeon.

Previous page: a group of turnstones with one purple sandpiper (foreground with spotted belly). This is a common grouping since both species occupy the same habitat – rocky coasts.

tion. Who knows how they discover such a favourable layer: perhaps it is a case of trial and error, or perhaps their in-built barometer has something to do with it. Birds are actually able to detect very small differences in air pressure.

Bar-tailed godwits fly non-stop from Siberia to the Wadden Sea.

Wind and weather Migrating birds take account of the weather in many other ways. They avoid bad weather – head winds, fog, precipitation – as far as possible. In such circumstances the birds will either not fly at all or they will land as soon as they possibly can if they are under way. Sometimes the birds cannot avoid bad weather but must fly through it, for example if it lasts for a long time. Certainly when the season is quite advanced there comes a point where time presses. It can also happen that birds flying over open sea are overtaken by rain or mist, when there is no alternative but to go on flying until they sight land. Along the coast you notice the arrival of groups of exhausted migrating birds.

On the coast of Groningen I once saw huge numbers of robins, redstarts, flycatchers, and other small song birds suddenly come down in thick fog. They landed on the first bit of solid land they could find – harbour breakwaters, the stone facing of the sea wall – because they were no longer in a fit state to find a tree or shrub.

Following page: redshank.

Some robins were so exhausted that they allowed themselves to be picked up. There are also many stories about birds that have had to

Bad weather. If it is more than a shower, migrating birds will land as soon as possible. Flying on costs unnecessary energy and brings the risk of ending up off course.

77

make an emergency landing on a ship. If the birds do not manage to reach land in time they are doomed to drown.

Storms can drive birds off course. From time to time in western Europe, particularly in the British Isles but also on the mainland, species are recorded that have come from America. In most cases they have been carried across the Atlantic by westerly storms. Such vagrants always attract a lot of attention from bird watchers.

Forster's tern: a vagrant from North America.

The greater yellowlegs is a North American migratory bird that occasionally arrives in Europe. Most of them land in Ireland and Great Britain. They are probably individuals that have been blown off course by storms and then have crossed the ocean.

Pages 80-81: a flock of snow geese.

Pages 82-83: greenshank.

How do birds find their way?

How do birds find their way and how do they manage to end up at exactly the same spot each year? These are questions that have occupied people for a very long time and into which a great deal of research has been done. They are looked at more closely in this chapter.

The red kite has been vigorously hunted and is therefore a timid and rare bird of prey.

There are countless examples of migratory birds that in spring return to precisely the same breeding site as the year before, sometimes year after year. The chiffchaff goes back to the same garden and the black-tailed godwit to the very same meadow. It makes no difference whether they have to come from southern Europe or from South Africa – the birds are able to locate their destination precisely over thousands of kilometres. Without maps and without signposts. How do they manage it?

This question has occupied researchers for a very long time.

Thousands of experiments have been carried out, often with birds in captivity. This work has yielded a great deal of information about the often unimaginable ability of birds to orientate themselves. But for the time being how exactly birds do orientate themselves remains a mystery.

Inborn characteristics

A young cuckoo has never seen its parents. In fact it has grown up in a foster family. Yet by itself it leaves at the right time and is able to find its way unerringly to the proper winter quarters – the region where cuckoos should spend the winter. How does it happen?

The example above makes it clear that a number of characters must almost certainly be inherited. The time of migration and the direction must be inherited, since the young cuckoo has not been able to learn them from anyone.

Opposite page: a young cuckoo.

Black-tailed godwits breed in damp meadows. A large part of the European population breeds in the Netherlands. They overwinter in west Africa, especially in the paddy fields of Senegal. They often return to exactly the same field in the spring.

Next page: avocet nest with young. Like all young waders avocets are nidifugous – they can run almost at once and quickly find their own food.

85

Instinctive direction   Tests that were conducted with birds kept in cages have indeed shown that it is a question of inborn characteristics.

From experiments with garden warblers that had been raised in captivity, it appeared that even alterations in the direction of migration are instinctive.

Wild garden warblers migrate first in a southwesterly direction to Spain, where they have to alter their course southwards in order to land in Africa and not over the ocean.

The caged garden warblers seemed to change their chosen direction from southwest to south, just about the time that their wild counterparts also had to do so!

Instinctive length of journey   Other tests showed that the length of the migration period is determined genetically, that is to say the period in which a bird has the urge to migrate.

This means that the bird finishes the journey at the correct time – namely when it has arrived in its winter quarters.

What it amounts to is that an instinctive direction combined with an instinctive length of journey will bring a young inexperienced bird "automatically" to its final destination. It sounds simple, but naturally it raises more questions. For example – the direction may be instinctive but how is a bird able to find that direction and hold it? In other words, how does a bird stay on course?

"Distraction display" of an avocet. By pretending that it has a broken wing the avocet tries to lead an invader away from its nest or its young.

Inbuilt compasses

It is not known exactly how birds do that. It is clear in any case that orientation on recognized fixed points – or beacons – on land plays little or no part.

It is also certain that birds possess various kinds of internal "compass." One of these is the sun compass.

Birds can orientate themselves according to the position of the sun. They have an internal clock with which they apply the appropriate correction as the position of the sun alters.

For night migrants, of course, a sun compass is no use as they navigate by the stars. This star compass works without correction.

Birds appear to be guided by a fixed point, the Pole Star and its immediate vicinity. They do not need to take any account of the rotation of the stars because the Pole Star is always in the north.

If, however, there is complete cloud cover birds can still navigate successfully. They are therefore able to do it without using the sun and star compasses.

This is thanks to the third type of compass they possess – the magnetic compass.

It is difficult for humans to imagine it, but birds can "feel" the earth's magnetic field and navigate by it. Birds use all three possibilities and probably others that nothing is known about.

It is completely unknown how they combine the compasses, whether they use them all at the same time or alternately, which is the most

Pair of avocets with young.

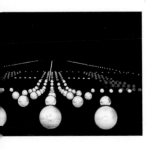

The runway of an airfield at night. Humans have developed technical aids to find the way. Birds can do just as well by themselves.

Pages 90-91: a flock of Bewick's swans.

Pages 92-93: curlews on the mud flats.

89

important, or whether they decide from situation to situation. In other words, there are still a lot of unanswered questions.

Starlings.

Finding the correct destination

It may be known roughly how birds navigate, but there is still no explanation of the fact that birds are able to find their exact goal.

Finding the exact destination involves a great deal more than simply choosing the right course and holding it.

In the 1950s the Dutch biologist Perdeck performed a classic, significant experiment.

Over a period of ten years he caught and ringed about ten thousand starlings in the vicinity of The Hague and had them transported by plane to Switzerland. They were released in Basle, Geneva, and Zurich. Since the wintering grounds of these starlings lie in south-eastern England and northern France, they normally migrate south-westwards.

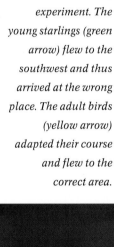

Perdeck's starling experiment. The young starlings (green arrow) flew to the southwest and thus arrived at the wrong place. The adult birds (yellow arrow) adapted their course and flew to the correct area.

In this case the young starlings held their course and flew to the southwest, landing in the south of France and northern Spain. They had therefore been following a compass course. In contrast the adult starlings flew towards the northwest, to their proper wintering grounds. Some actually succeeded in arriving there.

These older birds were thus able to reach their intended destination even when they were starting from a place where they had never been before!

The grey wagtail lives by fast-flowing water. In most areas it is a migrant, in some sedentary, and in others a partial migrant.

Finding the correct destination cannot therefore be a question of following recognizable points in the landscape. There is still no answer to the question of how birds can then find their goal from a random position.

All the conceivable possibilities have been tested experimentally, but up to now no proof has been found for a single theory.

The great white egret is about the same size as the grey heron. It is sparsely distributed in southeastern Europe. A pair of great white egrets breeds in the Netherlands – in the Oostvaardersplassen.

In the past the little egret was frequently shot for its plumes, which were much in demand for trimming ladies' hats.

Opposite page: the red-backed shrike.

Pages 98-99: the whiskered tern is a southern European marsh tern. It spends the winter in Africa and Asia.

Bird migration through the year

The concepts "spring migration" and "autumn migration" have been used in this book because they are now established terms, but in reality migration never comes to an end. All year round there are birds on passage somewhere in Europe.

Winter In January, in the depths of winter, it is relatively quiet on the bird front provided the weather is stable. At this time of year most birds stay more or less where they are. But as soon as the frost sets in that suddenly changes, with everywhere large flocks of birds moving about. They could consist of geese, swans, lapwings, golden plovers, starlings, thrushes, or chaffinches, all fleeing before the frost – preferably no further than necessary.

In very severe winters shallow coastal waters, such as the Wadden Sea, can freeze over. Then there will be a mass exodus especially of waders such as oystercatchers, curlews, and redshanks.
When England is in the grip of severe frost, many birds escape from England to Ireland, where the climate is much milder and the chances of survival are greater.

In mild weather the spring migration begins in February and early March. Skylarks, meadow pipits, lapwings, song thrushes, and mistle thrushes are then already under way to the north and northeast. These are true "weather birds" or species that have not been very far away and who follow the weather. Sometimes their excitement only lasts a short time – as soon as the frost returns they make an about turn. These to-and-fro movements can go on for quite a time, sometimes into April.

Golden plovers often show frost migration. If the frost sets in somewhere, they move on further; when the thaw comes they soon return. They are skilful fliers that can manoeuvre very well in large flocks.

Above left: the redshank is one of the species that joins in the great migration along the coast.

Spring In the spring it is the turn of the "calender birds." These are species that have overwintered far away, in southern Europe or Africa, and that return about the same time each year.

The timing of their migration has nothing to do with the weather in their breeding grounds. Bad weather can only delay their arrival for a day or two at the most.

The chiffchaff is one of the first summer visitors to return. It has spent the winter in the Mediterranean region and is usually present in most places when spring begins officially. It is soon followed by the willow warbler and the first swallows. These first swallows are the vanguard – the main company will come later. Hence the saying, "One swallow does not make a summer."

During April the other summer visitors arrive one by one, almost always in the same order.

The birds that have overwintered by the Mediterranean come first, and species that have to come from Africa, such as sparrowhawks and sedge warblers, arrive last.

Suddenly one day at the end of April or the beginning of May all the swifts are back. The golden oriole and the icterine warbler have just come back. The influx of summer birds continues throughout May. Even at the beginning of June, when most other birds are sitting on eggs, or even have young, there are still birds on the move.

The willow warbler is one of the earliest true summer birds to return.
It overwinters round the Mediterranean Sea. In the spring its sweet, rather melancholy song can be heard everywhere.

The first swallow is often already here in March, but one swallow does not make a summer. The main contingent comes later. The migration continues until well into May.

Following page: in mild winters oystercatchers overwinter in great numbers in the Wadden area. If it begins to freeze hard they leave in a body.

101

Summer   Simultaneously at the beginning of June the first movements begin in the opposite direction. About this time lapwings migrate from eastern Europe to the lowlands round the North Sea. Hard on their heels come starlings from roughly the same region.

In the case of the starlings it is the young birds, looking for good feeding grounds. In June the invasions of crossbills begin, reaching the peak in July.

In July, the height of summer, there is abundant evidence of "autumn migration." The summer visitors that were the last to arrive, such as the swifts and the golden oriole, are the first to leave. In August and September the first waders arrive from the far north. They congregate here before they migrate further in the direction of Africa. Most of the insect eaters – swallows, flycatchers, and reed warblers – depart for Africa. Most of them leave even more quietly than they arrived.

Starlings on an electricity pylon. When the last summer visitors are leaving, huge flocks of starlings arrive again from the east. Owners of cherry trees are well aware of it.

Autumn   In October most of the seed eaters, such as thrushes, chaffinches, wood pigeons, and skylarks, which remain in Europe, will migrate. Because these species mainly travel during the day, October is far and away the best month to observe bird migration. Bewick's swans, Brent geese, and many other water birds are now arriving from the far north.

The great daytime migration tails off in November.

Then new geese arrive – white-fronted and bean – and the lapwings

At the beginning of June, when the last summer visitors are returning, the first lapwings are already departing.

and golden plovers move on a little, especially if there is a severe frost for a day or two. In some years invasions of bramblings, siskins, and redpolls occur.

In December things are quiet once again. This quiet is however only relative, because it can be disturbed in January by frost migrations. Now there is only a month, or two months at the most, to wait before the first heralds of spring arrive.

In August thousands of black terns (foreground) from a large part of Europe congregate round the IJsselmeer before they migrate further towards Africa.

A flock of white-fronted geese.

Pages 106-107: Bewick's swans arriving from the tundra.

Page 108: a male redstart.

Page 109: the wood sandpiper.

Origin and evolution of bird migration

How bird migration originated is not known although it is certainly a very old phenomenon. Yet the present patterns of migration are not very old. Birds adapt their patterns to the changes which arise in all kinds of regions.

Developments around the Ice Age

It is highly likely that birds have been migrating as long as they have existed. Their ancestors also migrated, obviously not on the wing but by walking or swimming. This does not mean that present day bird migration has developed directly from bird migration then.

The present pattern of bird migration in Europe is not old, in fact it cannot date back more than about ten thousand years, which marks the end of the last Ice Age. Before then the climate in Europe was extremely cold.

The north was covered with snow and ice and the remainder as far as the Mediterranean was tree-less tundra. Africa, too, looked very different from the present day, since the area which is now the Sahara desert was green, moist, and fruitful.

It is inconceivable that the same bird species as nowadays used the same breeding grounds and visited the same wintering grounds via the same migration routes.

The current pattern of migration has thus developed since the Ice Age.

How the process took place is a matter for speculation. Species that had "escaped" to the south may perhaps have returned to their former, more northerly breeding grounds as the climate warmed up. Possibly they then had to leave them during the winter and return to the southern territories they had discovered later. Another possibility is that birds from tropical or subtropical regions took advantage of the

Black-winged stilts are mainly found in southern Europe, but occasionally they breed in the United Kingdom. They overwinter in Africa.

Previous page: nest of a common tern.

112

more favourable climate to extend in a northerly direction, although they were compelled to return south in the winter. Probably both processes took place.

More recent developments

Most patterns of migration, however, are much more recent, a few thousand years old at the most. After the end of the last Ice Age large climatic changes were still taking place. There were warm periods, interspersed with new cold ones. The boundaries between land and sea were constantly shifting owing to changes in sea level. It is certain that birds have adapted their range and their migration behaviour to these changes.

The range of a species is not fixed – boundaries are subject to change. Climatic changes are the most important elements which drive these adaptations.

At the moment temperatures are rising – when considered both on average and in the long term. This has meant that various species, such as the collared dove and the serin, have been able to extend their breeding range northwards in Europe during the twentieth century. Recently other species have undergone a similar development, for example the Mediterranean gull.

When other breeding areas were colonized the pattern of migration changed as well. There is no reason at all to suppose that birds would be less flexible in transferring their winter quarters. In Europe there is

The arctic redpoll is a paler relative of the redpoll. It breeds further north and usually spends the whole year in its breeding grounds. Occasionally a pair of arctic redpolls comes further south, sometimes with an invasion of redpolls.

The Mediterranean gull has extended its breeding grounds from southeastern to western Europe.

in fact a very good example available of a species that is in the process of altering its winter range.

The blackcap has taken over new winter quarters very rapidly. More and more blackcaps from Germany and Austria overwinter in the British Isles instead of in the Mediterranean region.

The changing migration behaviour of the blackcap

About 1970 blackcaps were recorded in winter in the British Isles for the first time. At first there was only the odd individual but each year there were more. They did not appear to be local breeding birds but members of the species from central Europe. They were actually accustomed to spending the winter in areas round the Mediterranean Sea. Meanwhile more than ten thousand blackcaps discovered the new winter quarters.

It probably happened as follows. The first blackcaps arrived in England through an accidental variation in course. It seemed that they could spend the winter there very comfortably thanks to the food put out for the birds. In most English gardens there is a bird-table with bread, fruit, and nuts. The blackcaps quickly learned to overcome their timidity and mingle with the tits, blackbirds, and sparrows. Because they only had a short distance to cover to return to their breeding grounds they arrived there earlier than their fellow blackcaps which were still bravely flying all the way to southern Europe for the winter. That meant that they had the advantage of choosing the best nesting sites, which probably gave them better breeding success. Presumably that was the key to the success of the new wintering grounds.

The scarlet rosefinch is an example of an eastern European species that is moving further westwards.

Opposite page: a penduline tit in the opening of its hanging nest.

114

Research into genetic variation

You have read in Chapter 6 that migration routes and destinations have been fixed by inheritance, but that is difficult to reconcile with the rapid changes in wintering grounds of the blackcap. That would mean that changes in inherited characters can also take place rapidly. That does not accord with current biological thinking that evolution is, on the contrary, a very slow and gradual process, and that certain changes take many generations, often centuries even.

That was enough for a group of German researchers under the leadership of Peter Berthold to subject the blackcap to closer investigation. In the winter they caught blackcaps in England and took them to south Germany, where they were kept in aviaries and were allowed to breed.

The young appeared, independently of the parents, to set a course for England. That provided the proof that the new direction of migration was indeed laid down in the genes.

How rapidly genetic changes can take place can be seen from experiments with blackcaps in the south of France. Part of the blackcap population in the south of France leaves, while the rest remains there during the winter. Again this difference is genetically determined – for each individual it is already determined in the egg whether it will be a migratory or a sedentary bird.

It seemed to be possible with selective breeding within three to six generations to raise a group consisting of either all migratory or all

Long-tailed ducks breed on tundra lakes and overwinter by the hundred thousand in the Baltic.

About 1930 the collared dove only occurred in the Balkans. Since then it has spread over the whole of Europe. It is now found even in northern Norway.

Opposite page: the greater flamingo.

117

sedentary birds from a mixed group of migratory and sedentary birds. The selection experiments mimic what happens naturally under the pressure for selection in changed circumstances. Essentially changes do not occur so rapidly in the wild.

Blackcaps that return in the spring to their breeding grounds in central Europe from the British Isles stay together – the rest are still in the south. They only pair up within the group and in that way the inherited tendency towards the new migration route can be extended rapidly. The blackcap has provided new insights, namely that evolution can occur much more quickly than was thought to be possible until very recently.

Nest of a common tern.

Future changes   Many more and greater changes are to be expected in the future. Scientists predict that the temperature of the earth will increase because of the greater volume of carbon dioxide released into the atmosphere by industry and traffic – the so-called greenhouse effect.

This greenhouse effect will have major consequences for the spread of birds. The warmer climate will play into the hands of the sedentary birds. Species that are at present partial migrants will develop into completely sedentary birds.

Distances between summer and winter quarters will become less, while those birds that migrate to Africa will have problems, since the area of desert is set to increase.

A mallard with young. In winter "our" mallards are replaced by birds from the north and east.

Perhaps they will be able to find a new wintering ground in southern Europe in time. If that is not the case, they will come off worst in the competition between sedentary birds and short-distance migrants.

The greater flamingo only breeds in a few places in the Mediterranean region, including the Camargue in the south of France. It is a migrant that overwinters in Africa and the Middle East.

The dipper lives beside fast-running water with a rocky bed. It migrates over short distances.

Pages 120-121: an ice-hole with water fowl.

pages 122-123: little stint.

Threats and protection

During the last hundred years birds have been under serious threat from industrialization, intensive farming, urbanization, and pollution. Moreover, migrating birds are still hunted in very many countries. It remains to be seen whether international discussions on bird protection will be effective.

Threats In the spring migration is less striking than in the autumn. The most important reason for this is that fewer birds are returning than left in the autumn. All kinds of dangers await the birds on migration. They can encounter fog and become disorientated, or bad weather over the sea or in the mountains, or be driven off course by storms. They may perhaps not find food in time, so that they cannot lay down enough reserves of fat to see them across the Mediterranean Sea and the Sahara in one hop. Very many migrating birds, however, fall victim to birds of prey and other predators. All these losses, however large they may be, are allowed for. Enough birds survive to maintain the population. That also applies to big disasters in which many birds perish in one event.

Just as sedentary birds can in time bring the population up to the normal level after having suffered heavy losses during a severe winter, migratory birds can also recover from a heavy blow. The "natural" disasters claim many victims, but do not threaten the survival of the species. From that point of view there is only one threat to birds and that is man.

A quarter of all species of birds in Europe are declining in numbers through human activity and are having serious problems.

Many of those species are migratory birds, including, please note, the species that enjoy the greatest popularity, such as the stork, the crane, and the swallow. The 1996 list of *Birds of Conservation Concern in*

The snipe is also part of the game bag. In the United Kingdom the breeding snipe – whose numbers are very much in decline – is protected.
In the Netherlands, however, the snipe that cross the country on migration are shot down.

Great Britain, Northern Ireland, the Isle of Man and the Channel Islands published by RSPB has 36 birds on the Red Data list of which five are migratory. One of the threats is hunting, but the damage to their habitats is even more crucial.

The teal is one of the species of duck that may be shot during the winter season in "developed" European countries such as the United Kingdom.

Hunting   The most direct human involvement in the life of migratory birds is hunting. Hunting mirgratory birds is a mass sport in the countries round the Mediterranean Sea. The extent of it defies description. In Italy alone it is roughly estimated that 200 million birds are killed annually. In Greece and Turkey, on Malta and Cyprus, millions of birds are shot or trapped every year. There is no end to the inventiveness employed. All kinds and gauges of nets are used, together with decoys and fake bushes that have the branches smeared with birdlime.

A shooting box. Everywhere in Europe harmless migratory birds are still hunted. It happens mainly in France and southern countries.

In France, too, hunting migrating birds is popular. French hunters shoot at almost everything that flies. They shoot sandpipers, black-tailed godwits, and even spoonbills and cranes are not safe there. Species that enjoy special protection in, for example, Scandinavia, Germany, the Netherlands, and Great Britain, are shown no mercy in France.

Unfortunately the migrants that do emerge from Europe all in one piece run, if possible, even more risks in Africa.

Wildfowlers. Shooting does not only cause direct damage but also causes disturbance to resting migratory birds.

In the Scandinavian countries, and countries such as Germany and the United Kingdom, most migratory birds are protected. But even here the situation is not perfect. In each country completely harmless migratory birds may be hunted.

In the United Kingdom, for instance, some duck and snipe may be shot. Hunting forms a serious threat to migratory species that only occur in small numbers and which, in addition, migrate in narrow bands where hunters can easily intecept them.

That applies, for example, to birds of prey such as the imperial eagle, Egyptian vulture, and Bonelli's eagle. For most other species the impact of hunting is difficult to quantify. It is almost always a combination of factors that leads to the decline of a bird population. hunting is one of these, but even if the number of victims is enormous, it is not usually the main cause.

Industrial expansion threatens important bird areas.

Damage to habitats

Far and away the most serious threat to migratory birds is the damage to their habitats. Especially during the last hundred years the European landscape has been radically altered by human activity, such as industrialization, road building, urban expansion, and pollution. The changes are taking place more and more rapidly, and on a larger and larger scale.

Damage to the habitat is the primary cause of the decline and extinction of plants and animals over the whole world.

The landscape of the future. Is there still a place here for migratory birds?

Birds, too, do not escape, however great their capacity for adaptation may be – the changes are taking place too rapidly and on too large a scale. That applies just as much to sedentary as to migratory birds. The special point about migratory birds is that they cross a whole range of habitats, and can therefore encounter problems not only in their breeding grounds but also in their winter quarters and on passage.

Economic and technological developments

The changes occurred first and were the most extensive in the rich countries of western Europe. The economic and technological development and the growth of prosperity came at a price. Practically all nature has been sacrificed.

Almost nothing remains of the once widespread wetlands – marshes were difficult areas that you could well do without. Lakes, pools, river banks, and deltas were drained and reclaimed. The remaining fragments became polluted and dried out.

Then it was the turn of southern Europe, and here too the loveliest river deltas were done away with in the name of progress, for example the Ebro delta in Spain or the Evros on the border of Greece and Turkey. It is not surprising that water and marsh birds are experiencing serious problems.

The black tern, the purple heron, the squacco herons and night herons are just a few examples of bird species for which less and less living and breeding space is available.

A red-throated diver, washed ashore, a victim of fuel oil.

The timid purple heron breed in colonies in extensive reedbeds. Many of these have vanished, so that the species is in the Red Data Book. Commercial reed production does not favour the purple heron.

Following page: the squacco heron breeds chiefly in fresh-water marshes in the south-east of Europe. Unfortunately numbers are declining greatly.

127

History is now being repeated in eastern Europe. Eastern Europe was for a long time a backward area where paradises for birds were left relatively undisturbed.

People in these countries now want to join in world trade, on the western pattern and as rapidly as possible. The mistakes that were made in the west are being repeated and apparently nothing at all has been learned from the past.

Developments in agriculture

The same goes for the agricultural regions. A large part of Europe is agricultural. About fifty years ago agriculture was still small scale and environmentally friendly and there was room for plants and animals. After the Second World War that changed very rapidly. Western Europe was also in the forefront here. Mechanization, artificial fertilizer, and pesticides, drainage and irrigation allowed an unprecedented increase in the scale and intensity of agriculture. Everything was directed towards greater production. As a result the habitats of the birds were impoverished.

The summer song of the skylark belongs to the European countryside, but how much longer will people be able to enjoy it? Developments in agriculture have led to a steep decline in numbers.

Hedges, wooded banks, and ditches disappeared and there was less and less space for weeds, insects, and small mammals which meant less and less food for the birds. The storks disappeared. The numbers of lark in countries such as Great Britain have been halved in twenty years. The swallow, red-backed shrike, and a whole series of other species are loosing ground.

A male garganey. The gargeney is a small, elegant duck that breeds in marshy areas and overwinters in Africa. Its numbers are declining for all kinds of reasons – loss of breeding habitat, drainage, disturbance, lead poisoning, and shooting.

Although agriculture threatens to be overwhelmed by its own success – overproduction, environmental problems, decline in the number of farms, people leaving the countryside – the developments are continuing just the same.

The developments in agricultural technology are even being exported. The last beautiful old cultural landscapes in Spain are being sacrificed to large-scale agriculture, and yet more overproduction, with millions of pounds in subsidies from the European Union. Now that southern Europe is running farming more and more on the western European model it is the turn of eastern Europe. Now there are still areas there where you can see how it used to be in the west – fields full of quail, corncrakes, and corn buntings. But you must be quick if you want to see it, because the developments are being implemented at a great pace.

International bird protection

A great deal more needs to be done to give migratory birds better protection. That can only happen through international cooperation – damage to the wintering grounds or important stopping places will make protecting a species in its breeding habitat come to nothing. To protect migratory birds, the whole of their living environment must be protected.

On paper this need for protection is in general recognized. The number of organisations involved in the protection of migratory birds is

The quail hides in rough pastures and crops during the breeding season and its presence is only betrayed by its call of "whic, whic." One year there are many quail, the next almost none. The numbers are, however, declining because with modern agricultural methods of intensive cultivation and the use of pesticides the quail can no longer hold its own.

amazingly large. Governments of European countries have signed nice agreements. The Ramsar Convention in 1971 – named after the place in Iran where the convention was held – obliged states to protect wetland habitats that were of international importance for birds. In 1979 the EC bird directive was issued, which states that all EC countries must take account of the needs of birds in their legislation. In 1982 the Bern Convention, which is directed towards nature conservation in general, came into force. Yet again, in 1983 the Bonn Convention was added, which is specially concerned with migratory animal species.

There is therefore no lack of good intentions and fine words, but the implementation falls very much short of both. At present less than 30 per cent of the important areas for birds in Europe are regarded as protected.

In areas which are said to be protected pollution and drainage often continue as usual.

The Wadden Sea, which is so important as a resting ground for water birds on the eastern Atlantic migration route, enjoys international recognition second to none. It has almost every conceivable designation of legal and formal protection and yet nature is under pressure on all sides.

Industry is expanding, there is drilling for natural gas, recreation is increasing, and overfishing is taking place.

Modern large-scale farming.

The turtle dove is a bird that lives in areas of small-scale, varied cultivation. Numbers are declining because of shooting and the intensification of agriculture.

The corncrake is even more secretive than the quail. It is one of the rails which lives mainly in hay meadows and sometimes in cornfields, and is rarely seen. It betrays itself especially at night by its rasping croak of "crex crex." The corncrake is a species under threat worldwide. The most important cause is the disappearance of "old-fashioned" hay meadows. In the past mowing took place earlier and more often.

But designating nature reserves is not enough in itself. Even if all the important bird habitats are protected effectively, many migratory birds will not survive as long as the quality of our environment continues to decline.

Migratory birds are a barometer for the state of the environment. When the number of migratory birds declines, you can be certain that there is also something amiss with other forms of life. In more and more places people watch in vain in spring for the return of the stork. If we want to prevent that happening to the skylark and the swallow there will have to be radical changes made to the way the environment is being treated.

The edge of a field with poppies and other wild flowers alongside an unmetalled road.

Pages 134-135: greater flamingos.

Pages 136-137: Sandwich terns (left of centre) are rare and under threat.

Bibliography

The following books were consulted in the course of writing this book:

Alerstam, T., *Bird Migration*, Cambridge University Press, 1990.

Berthold, P., *Bird Migration, a general survey*, Oxford University Press, 1993.

Cramp, S., *et al.*, *Handbook of the Birds of Europe, the Middle East and North Africa*, volumes 1-9, Oxford University Press, 1977-1994.

Information on the decline of migratory birds and the causes of it is taken mainly from:

Tucker, G. M. & Heath, M.F., *Birds in Europe: Their Conservation Status*, Bird Life International, Cambridge, 1994.

For the English edition:

Peterson, R.T., Mountfort, G. & Hollom, P.A.D. *Birds of Britain and Europe*, Harper Collins, 1993.

Porter, R., *Wild Birds and the Law*, RSPB, 1993.

Birds of Conservation Concern, RSPB, 1996.

Photo credits

J. Boshuizen, Amsterdam: pages 26, 55 above, 58 above, 119 below.

H. Hut, Ten Boer: title page, pages 4, 6 right, 7, 8, 9, 10-11, 12, 13, 14, 15, 16-17, 18, 20 right, 21, 23, 24-25, 27, 28–29, 30-31, 33, 34 above, 35 above, 36-37, 38, 39 below, 40-41, 43, 44, 45 below, 46-47, 48-49, 50-51, 53 above, 55 below, 57 below, 58 below, 59, 60 above, 61 below, 63 below, 64-65, 6667, 69, 70, 71 above, 72, 73, 74-75, 76, 77, 80-81, 82-83, 86-87, 88, 89, 90-91, 92-93, 94, 95, 96, 97, 98-99, 100 right, 101, 102-103, 104 above, 105, 106-107, 109, 110-111, 112, 114, 115, 116, 117 below, 118, 119 above, 120-121, 122-123, 124, 125, 126, 127, 128-129, 130 above, 131, 132 above, 133, 134-135, 136-137.

J. van Holten, Schiedam: pages 19, 22 above, 34 below, 35 below, 39, above, 45 above, 52, 53 below, 57 above, 61 above, 62 above, 63 above, 68, 71 below, 79, 84, 85, 100 left, 108, 113, 117 above, 130 below, 132 below.

J. v. d. Leijgraaf, Huissen: pages 6 left, 20 left, 22 below, 60 below, 62 below, 78, 104 below.

The translator is grateful to Dr S.A. Hinsley, of ITE, Monks Wood for advice in the preparation of this edition.

Index of scientific names

Index of common English names